# This igloo book belongs to:

**igloobooks**

*Published in 2016*
*by Igloo Books Ltd*
*Cottage Farm*
*Sywell*
*NN6 0BJ*
*www.igloobooks.com*

*LEO002 0616*
*2 4 6 8 10 9 7 5 3 1*
*ISBN 978-1-78557-739-0*

*Printed and manufactured in China*

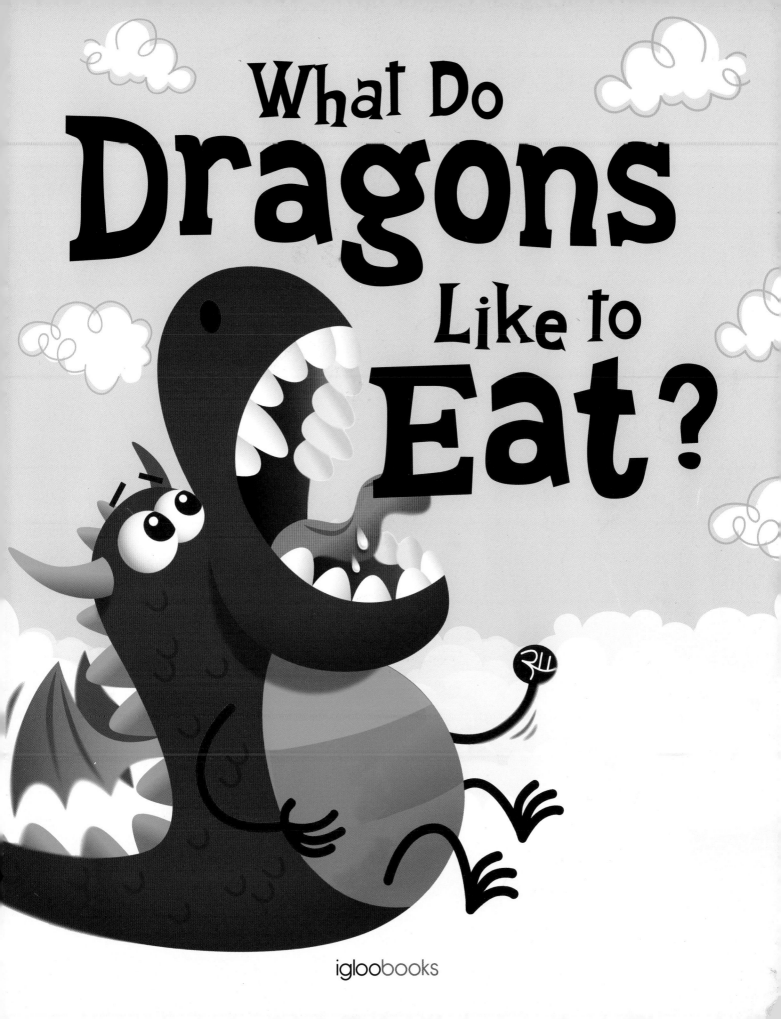

# What Do Dragons Like to Eat?

igloobooks

# What do dragons like to eat?
## Is it salty? Is it sweet?

## Potato crisps and lemon pie.

Ham, mustard and cheese on rye.

Peanut butter and jam, too!
Bubblegum to pop and chew.

Milkshake and chicken wings,
dragons eat almost anything!

Sir Danby is a different beast.
The way he feels affects his feast.

Depending on his dragon mood,
he has a different favourite food!

When Sir Danby is feeling mad,
he starts to act a little bad.

He breathes out fire and things get hot.
Look! He roars, that hits the spot!

# And if Sir Danby is feeling silly, the only food he wants is chilli!

He starts to giggle and laughter grows.
The chilli might come out of his nose!

But sometimes Sir Danby is feeling blue.
Then he only asks for stew.

Beef or fish, it doesn't matter,
just be sure to bring a platter!

And when he's cheered up all the way,
Sir Danby craves a whole buffet.

He fills his plate to the tip-top,
then washes it down with fizzy pop!

When it's time to celebrate,
a slice of cake goes on his plate.

Instead of blowing the candles out,
he lights them with his fiery snout!

# What is Sir Danby's favourite meal?
## It doesn't matter how he feels.

When he's with his favourite guests,
a meal with friends is always best!